Artists: **YUSAKU KOMIYAMA** & **JIM CAMPBELL** (#1) and **KIICHI MIZUSHIMA** (#2-3, #0)

ON EDITOR: **Jeff Youngquist** EXECUTIVE EDITORS: **C.B. Cebulski** & **Tom Brevoort** ASSISTANT EDITOR: **Caitlin O'Connell**
E MANAGER, DIGITAL ASSETS: **Joe Hochstein** SENIOR EDITOR, SPECIAL PROJECTS: **Jennifer Grünwald**
E MANAGING EDITOR: **Kateri Woody** EDITOR, SPECIAL PROJECTS: **Mark D. Beazley** SVP PRINT, SALES & MARKETING: **David Gabriel**
ON: **Ryan Devall** & **Joe Frontirre** DESIGNER: **Jay Bowen**

Writer/Artist: **YUSAKU KOMIYAMA** • Script: **JIM ZUB** • Letters: **VC's TRAVIS LANHAM**

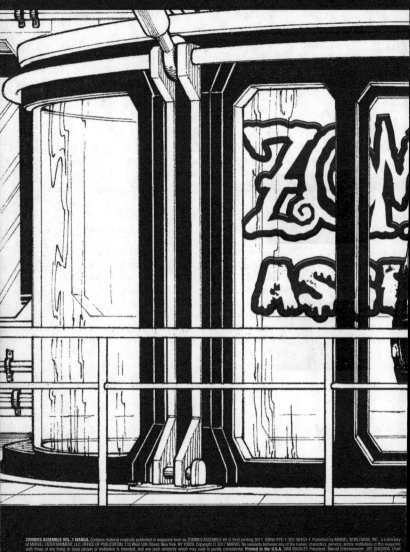

ZOMBIES ASSEMBLE VOL. 1 MANGA. Contains material originally published in magazine form as ZOMBIES ASSEMBLE #0-3. First printing 2017. ISBN# 978-1-302-90453-1. Published by MARVEL WORLDWIDE, INC., a subsidiary of MARVEL ENTERTAINMENT, LLC. OFFICE OF PUBLICATION: 135 West 50th Street, New York, NY 10020. Copyright © 2017 MARVEL. No similarity between any of the names, characters, persons, and/or institutions in this magazine with those of any living or dead person or institution is intended, and any such similarity which may exist is purely coincidental. **Printed in the U.S.A.** DAN BUCKLEY, President, Marvel Entertainment; JOE QUESADA, Chief Creative Officer; TOM BREVOORT, SVP of Publishing; DAVID BOGART, SVP of Business Affairs & Operations, Publishing & Partnership; C.B. CEBULSKI, VP of Brand Management & Development, Asia; DAVID GABRIEL, SVP of Sales & Marketing, Publishing; JEFF YOUNGQUIST, VP of Production & Special Projects; DAN CARR, Executive Director of Publishing Technology; ALEX MORALES, Director of Publishing Operations; SUSAN CRESPI, Production Manager; STAN LEE, Chairman Emeritus. For information regarding advertising in Marvel Comics or on Marvel.com, please contact Vit DeBellis, Integrated Sales Manager, at vdebellis@marvel.com. For Marvel subscription inquiries, please call 888-511-5480. **Manufactured between 9/15/2017 and 10/17/2017 by SHERIDAN, CHELSEA, MI, USA.**

10 9 8 7 6 5 4 3 2 1

THOR

REAL NAME:
Thor Odinson

Thor is the Asgardian
god of Thunder and
an Avenger. Wielding
Mjolnir, a mystical Uru
hammer of immense
power, the son of Odin
acts to protect Earth
and all the Nine Realms.

HAWKEYE

REAL NAME:
Clint Barton

Former criminal Clint
Barton used his circus
training to become the
greatest sharpshooter
the world has ever
seen. He reformed and
joined the Avengers,
quickly becoming one
of the team's most
stalwart members.

BLACK WIDOW

REAL NAME:
Natasha Romanoff

Natasha Romanoff is
a deadly operative
equipped with state-of-
the-art weaponry and
extensive hand-to-hand
combat training. Before
joining S.H.I.E.L.D. and
the Avengers, she was
an enemy spy; now, she
uses her unique skills to
atone for her past.

IRON MAN

REAL NAME:
Anthony Edward Stark

Billionaire playboy and genius industrialist Tony Stark was kidnapped during a routine weapons test. His captors attempted to force him to build a weapon of mass destruction. Instead, he created a powerful suit of armor that saved his life. From that day on, he has used the suit to protect the world as the invincible Avenger Iron Man.

CAPTAIN AMERICA

REAL NAME:
Steven Rogers

During World War II, a secret military experiment turned scrawny Steve Rogers into America's first Super-Soldier, Captain America. Near the end of the war, Rogers was presumed dead in an explosion over the English Channel. Decades later, Cap was found frozen in ice and was revived. Steve Rogers awakened to a world he never imagined—a man out of time. He again took up the mantle of Captain America, defending the United States and the world from threats of all kinds.

HULK

REAL NAME:
Bruce Banner

Bruce Banner was a brilliant scientist working for the Army when he was caught in the explosion of a gamma bomb of his own creation and transformed into the nearly indestructible Hulk. Now, Dr. Banner struggles to control his anger and anxiety to keep the Hulk in check while he fights alongside the Avengers.

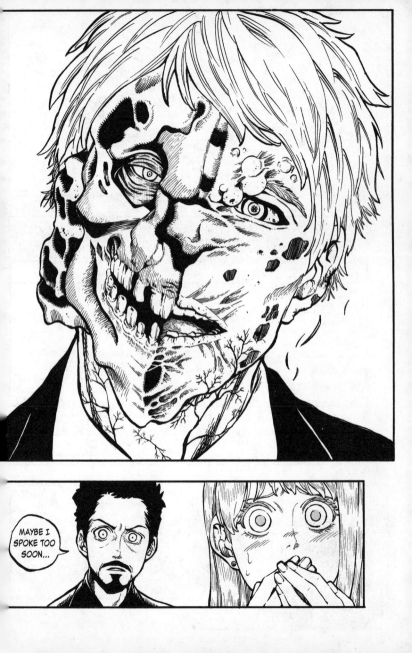

MAYBE I SPOKE TOO SOON...

* J.A.R.V.I.S. (JUST A RATHER VERY INTELLIGENT SYSTEM)--TONY STARK'S ARTIFICIALLY INTELLIGENT ASSISTANT.

UNDERSTOOD.

OKAY, AS FAR AS I CAN TELL, THERE ARE LESS THAN A DOZEN ZOMBIES HERE IN THE BUILDING, BUT WE'VE STILL GOT TO BE CAREFUL. THE LAST THING WE NEED IS AN OUTBREAK.

グリシャン
THOOOM!

THOSE PEOPLE OUTSIDE ARE COUNTING ON US.

YOU'RE THE ONLY ONE WHO CAN PICK IT UP, REMEMBER?

YOU BETTER GRAB YOUR HAMMER.

UH, TONY...

AH, YES.

VERILY.

THIS IS A DISASTER.

I KNOW, BRUCE. I'M JUST TRYING NOT TO BRING IT UP RIGHT NOW. IF THOR FREAKS OUT, HE COULD PROBABLY TAKE US ALL DOWN...

...SO EVERYONE STAY CALM.

THOR'S CLEARLY BEEN INFECTED BY THIS ZOMBIE VIRUS!

AREN'T YOU GOING TO SAY SOMETHING?

YES?

NATASHA.

HMM...

WHERE DID IT COME FROM?

WHAT IS THIS?

IT'S QUITE STRIKING IN ITS APPEARANCE.

MAYHAP IT IS ONE OF YOUR BEAUTY ACCESSORIES?

IS THIS ORB YOURS?

BASED ON WHAT EVIDENCE?

YOU DID?

WHAT ARE WE GOING TO DO TO STOP THIS VIRUS AND CURE THOR?

ENOUGH BRAGGING.

FIRST THINGS FIRST.

I FIGURED OUT HOW THE VIRUS IS BEING SPREAD.

LEAVE THE SCIENCE TO GENIUSES LIKE BANNER AND ME. I DON'T TELL YOU HOW TO DO SPY STUFF...

THAT'S A FACT.

A BITE ISN'T REQUIRED.

THOR WASN'T BITTEN.

I DOUBT TEETH COULD PIERCE HIS ASGARDIAN FLESH.

LOOKING AT IT AS A ZOMBIE OUTBREAK, IT WOULD BE EASY TO ASSUME THE VIRUS IS TRANSMITTED BY BITE.

BUT THAT'S A MISTAKE.

YOU'RE NOT WORRIED ABOUT ME, ARE YOU?

I DIDN'T KNOW YOU CARED, GREEN GUY.

HEY, BRUCE.

NATASHA...

NATASHA...

SHOOOM!

KHEEE!

DON'T MAKE JOKES, NOT NOW.

THIS IS DEADLY SERIOUS.

SURVEILLANCE CAMERA FOOTAGE FROM MADISON AVENUE AND EAST 32ND.

ENTIRE SECTIONS OF NEW YORK ARE BEING OVERRUN.

BUT THERE'S A MORE LIKELY SCENARIO...

POSSIBLY.

THE VIRUS HAS ALREADY ESCAPED.

IT'S HORRIFYING.

BRRR-RING!

BRRR-RING!

TONY

TONY! ARE YOU OKAY?!

COLONEL JAMES "RHODEY" RHODES
ONE OF TONY STARK'S BEST FRIENDS.

AN UPDATE? SURE.

OKAY, SORRY, CAN YOU GIVE ME AN UPDATE?

LET ME GIVE YOU THE EXPEDITED VERSION.

NO NEED TO FREAK OUT, RHODEY.

OKAY, TONY...

WHAT DO YOU KNOW ABOUT THE ZOMBIE VIRUS?

IT...IT WAS A MISTAKE.

THE CHITAURI CELL MATTER...

...IT MUTATED IN WAYS I NEVER ANTICIPATED.

I NEVER INTENDED FOR ANY OF THIS TO HAPPEN.

TONY, DON'T ANTAGONIZE HER.

ACCIDENT OR NOT...YOU STARTED ALL THIS, IT'S YOUR FAULT, LADY.

THERE WERE TRACES ON THE WEAPON I OBTAINED.

HOW DID YOU GET CHITAURI CELL SAMPLES IN THE FIRST PLACE?

MY BAG WITH THE CELL MATTER WAS STOLEN WHEN I TOOK THE SUBWAY.

I DIDN'T HIRE HER, REMEMBER? NOT MY FAULT.

SHE'S YOUR SCIENTIST!

AS OWNER OF THE COMPANY, YOU ARE TECHNICALLY RESPONSIBLE.

SHUT UP, J.A.R.V.I.S.!

SOME PEOPLE ARE JUST TOO SMART FOR THEIR OWN GOOD.

I'VE SEEN IT ALL BEFORE.

I CAN'T BELIEVE YOU CAUSED ALL THIS. SO RECKLESS...

HOLD ON!

IT'S TRUE.

WE NEED TO FOCUS ON CREATING AN ANTI-VIRUS AND VACCINE.

WE DON'T HAVE TIME TO ARGUE ABOUT BLAME RIGHT NOW.

HARD TO SAY.

IT SEEMED TO WORK FOR A BIT, BUT THEN QUICKLY DISSIPATED.

WHAT HAPPENED WITH DR. AMANO'S ANTIDOTE? DO YOU THINK IT'S A FAKE?

WE'RE LUCKY THAT SEDATIVE WORKED, I USED EIGHT TIMES THE NORMAL DOSAGE.

EVEN STILL, HE COULD WAKE UP AT ANY TIME AND GO BERSERK AGAIN.

THAT WAS A CLOSE ONE...

WHEW TOO CLOSE

は ぁ.

は ぁ.

WE NEED BOTH OF YOU IN HERE.

GENTS.

WE'LL NEED HER HELP TO PRODUCE A VIABLE ANTIVIRUS.

SHE KNOWS MORE ABOUT THIS VIRUS THAN WE DO.

BLOP ぶく BLOP ぶく

NO SIGNAL, SIR.

THE TRANSMISSION ENDED ABRUPTLY.

J.A.R.V.I.S., WHAT IS GOING ON?!

BWIP

RHODEY?!

RHODEY!

...A BLAST.

ME, TOO.

IT SOUNDED LIKE...

I HEARD SOMETHING BEFORE IT CUT OUT.

OKAY, TEAM, LET'S CHECK IT OUT!

DR. AMANO, ANY THEORIES ON WHAT THIS IS?

UNFORTUNATELY, NO. MY EXPERIMENTS WERE LIMITED.

WAIT A SEC--YOU THINK RHODEY'S CREW WAS ATTACKED?

DO THESE ZOMBIES HAVE BOMBS NOW?

NO, IF IT DIDN'T WORK AND WE LOST HER, I...

WE'VE GOT TO SAVE THIS MOMENT!

THE GREATEST INVENTION OF THE MODERN WORLD UNFOLDING IN REAL TIME!

HEY! JASPER, C'MON! DON'T RECORD THIS!

I LOOK TERRIBLE AFTER ALL THESE LATE NIGHTS!

WHY DIDN'T SHE MENTION THAT BEFORE?

SHE DIDN'T WORK ALONE?

OKAY, OKAY...

WE'LL DO IT LATER! LET'S GET SOME FOOD!

THIS MUST BE WHEN SHE FOUND THE VIRUS.

"JASPER"... "GREATEST INVENTION OF THE MODERN WORLD"...

!!

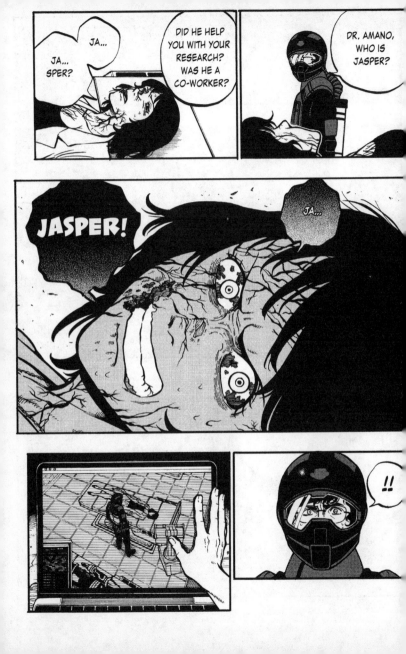

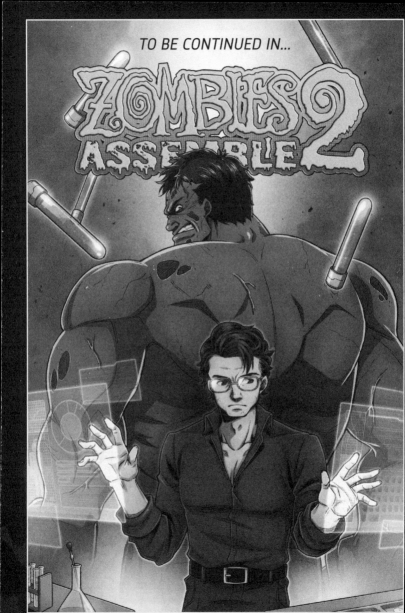

READING MINDS IS NOT ONE OF MS. POTTS' MANY SKILLS.

EXPRESSING HOW YOU FEEL MAY BE HELPFUL.

SIR...

I'LL TAKE CARE OF IT ON MY OWN.

SHE'S GOT MORE IMPORTANT THINGS TO DEAL WITH.

DULY NOTED, SIR.

KEEP TALKING LIKE THAT AND I'M GOING TO START THINKING YOU'RE HUMAN.

SPEAKING OF HUMANITY, AREN'T YOU COLD?

NO, I'M FINE.

YEAH, YEAH. I DON'T CARE.

THERE ARE HEALTH CONCERNS...

WHY'S THAT?

PUTTING ON A SHIRT IS ADVISABLE.

OKAY, LET'S CHANGE THE SUBJECT.

WHAT ABOUT THAT LETTER YOU RECEIVED?

BESIDES, YOU'RE A DOCTOR! YOU'VE GOTTA KEEP MY CASE CONFIDENTIAL!

NO WAY!

DO YOU WANT ME TO TELL HER FOR YOU?

OKAY.

I'M NOT AN MD.

WHAT AN ASS.

KNOWING YOU...

...I'M GUESSING YOU DIDN'T SHARE IT WITH HER.

...BE HONEST.

HERE'S SOME ADVICE...

THINK CAREFULLY ABOUT THAT.

TONY...
I DON'T
KNOW HOW
YOU DO
IT...

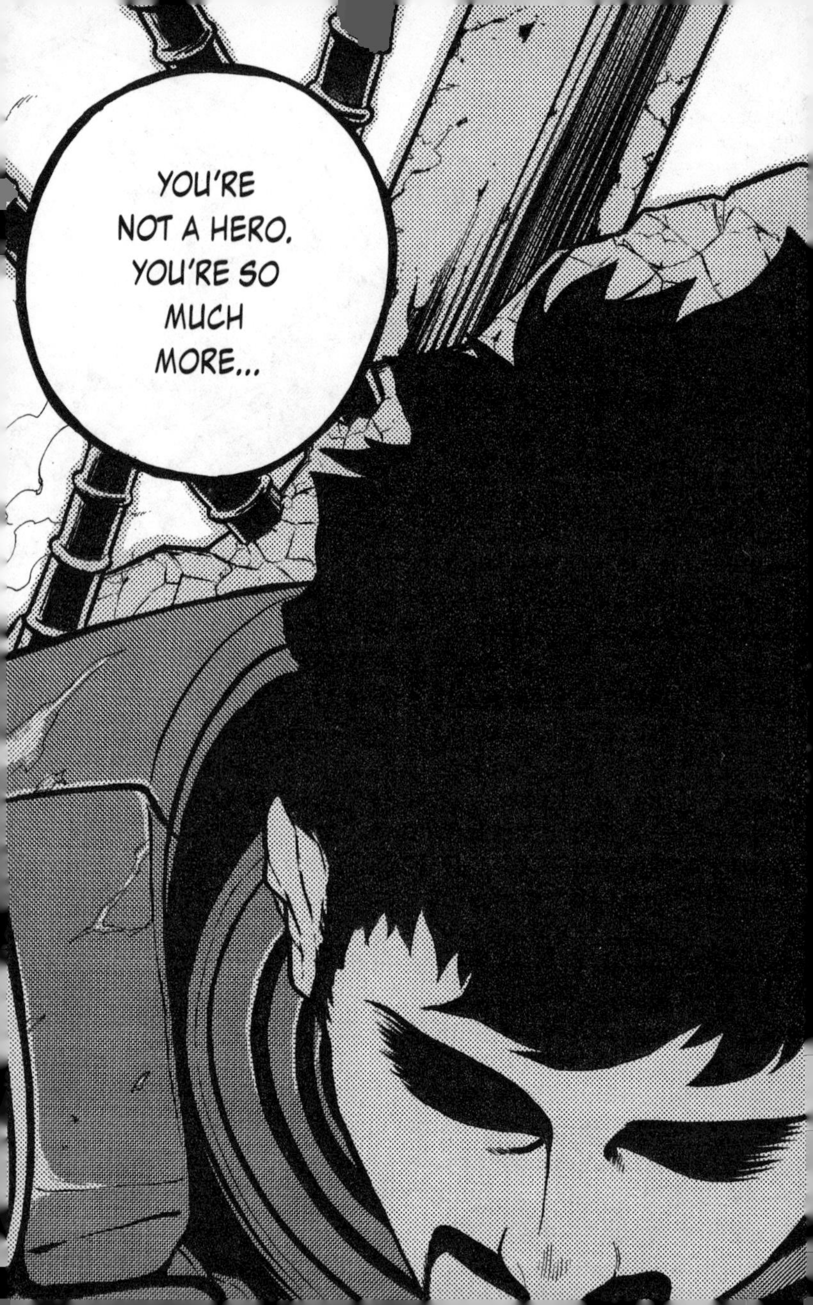
YOU'RE NOT A HERO. YOU'RE SO MUCH MORE...

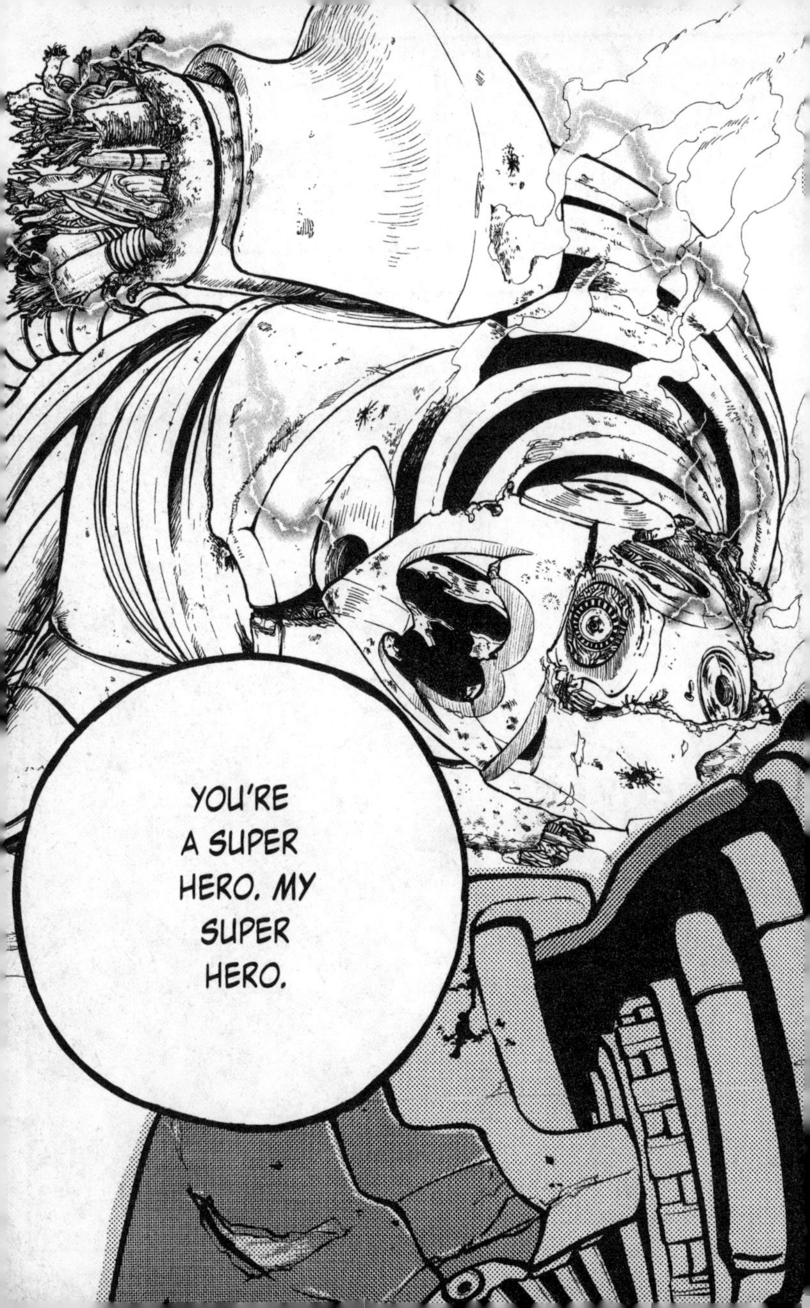
YOU'RE A SUPER HERO. MY SUPER HERO.

#2 VARIANT BY **GREG HORN**

#3 VARIANT BY **GREG LAND**, **JAY LEISTEN** & **DAVID CURIEL**

#0 VARIANT BY **DAVID NAKAYAMA**

#0 VARIANT BY **NIC KLEIN**

MARVEL: Let's test your undead cred: top five zombie movies—go!

ZUB: That's easy: *Zombieland, 28 Days Later, Shaun of the Dead, Dawn of the Dead, Night of the Living Dead.*

MARVEL: Now that is a pretty definitive movie marathon right there. It has to be asked though, what do you prefer: classic, shambling *Night of the Living Dead* zombies, or fast-moving *28 Days Later* rage monsters?

ZUB: I liked *28 Days Later* as a film, but I prefer slow and steady when it comes to zombie movement. The relentless inhuman shamble is far scarier to me than acrobatic, sprinting zombies.

MARVEL: Now, talking films isn't exactly off-topic, because this book features the cast of the *Avengers* movies. The Marvel Cinematic Universe has blended super heroics with a number of different genres so far—why not full-on horror?

ZUB: I know it's not in the MCU, but *Blade* sort of counts, right? Those are super-heroic horror films. That said, I think it's just a matter of time before the MCU digs into Marvel's wonderful horror canon. I'd love to see *Werewolf by Night, Morbius, Man-Thing,* or *Moon Knight* join the MCU.

MARVEL: You are not alone there! With *Zombies Assemble*, it isn't just the characters that are drawn from the films, but the actual plague in effect in this story is drawn from the plot of that first *Avengers* film. Did that particularly interest you as a fresh spin on the undead concept?

ZUB: It's really weird, a bit like *Avengers* fan fiction run amok. I love that this just played as a sequel to the *Avengers* movies, building on the MCU continuity but pulling it all sideways into this strange horror story. It shouldn't work, but you end up feeling those familiar notes from the movies and can't help but enjoy the ride.

MARVEL: You also get to play with the relationships between the characters, which is one of the major strengths of the *Avengers* films. Are there any you particularly enjoyed writing?

ZUB: The budding romance between Banner and Natasha is a real focal point, which was nice to see. I hope that's something the movies don't shy away from down the line.

MARVEL: Was this project good practice for taking over the *Uncanny Avengers* book? Any plans to unleash the undead on them any time soon? Seems a natural fit with Doctor Voodoo on the team...

ZUB: *Zombies Assemble* is totally different in scope and tone from what I'm doing with *Uncanny Avengers*, but I can honestly say that every writing project I work on teaches me something new about storytelling, pacing, and characterization—so it's all relative. That said, Doctor Voodoo will be dealing with some upcoming possession stuff, so anything's possible!

MARVEL: You're obviously a fan of manga artwork...

ZUB: I'm a fan of well-done art in any style. Good storytelling, solid character work, well-drawn environments. I try not to box things in as "manga" or "not manga" when it comes to art styles. So many contemporary comic artists are influenced by mangaka, and I love seeing that subtly (or not-so-subtly) showing up in more North American comics.

MARVEL: Yusaku Komiyama definitely ticks the box, artistically. What are some of your favorite images/scenes in this book?

ZUB: It's always fun seeing iconic characters in different styles, and Yusaku Komiyama's work on *Zombies Assemble* is no exception. Komiyama's version of the MCU is instantly recognizable, but has its own flair. The characters look like their live-action counterparts, but their expressions are a bit broader and more playful. The artist mixes the creepy factor of big zombie moments well with silly or romantic moments. Komiyama loves these characters and wants to do right by them even while pushing them into a crazy story we'll never see on the silver screen. The sequence where Rhodey is talking to Tony about the zombie situation while Tony and Clint are fighting Zombie Thor cracks me up every time I see it. It feels like a classic Iron Man moment: Tony keeping his cool and staying confident even while everything's going nuts all around him.

MARVEL: Classic Tony indeed. But let's put you inside Steve's head, instead. Imagine this: You're Captain America, leading the Avengers, and you hear that Thanos and Loki have invaded Manhattan, while a zombie outbreak has begun in Washington, D.C. Where do you point the Quinjet?

ZUB: I'd cheat and split up the team for maximum coverage. Thor, Hulk, and Iron Man can fly or leap to Manhattan to hold off Thanos and Loki while Cap, Black Widow, and Hawkeye tackle the zombie hordes and try to rally backup with other heroes or the Army. If we've got Spider-Man, Vision, Scarlet Witch, Falcon, and Ant-Man on board as well, even better. The Avengers are going to save everyone because that's what great heroes do.

MARVEL: Spoken like a true leader! Many thanks, Jim—and may your days be free from grotesque hordes of humanity gone berserk!

ZUB DUBS THE AVENGERS!

BY JESS HARROLD

IT FALLS TO CANADIAN WRITER JIM ZUB TO ADAPT THE JAPANESE *ZOMBIES ASSEMBLE* FOR AN AMERICAN AUDIENCE—AND THE REST OF THE ENGLISH-SPEAKING WORLD! IT'S A TRULY INTERNATIONAL OPERATION, AS ZUB (*FIGMENT*, *THUNDERBOLTS*) TAKES A LITERAL TRANSLATION OF THE MANGA AND REINTERPRETS THE DIALOGUE IN THE MIGHTY MARVEL MANNER. HERE ZUB TALKS ABOUT THE PROCESS, AND HOW THE PROJECT COMBINES THREE THINGS HE LOVES: JAPANESE CULTURE, SUPER HEROES, AND—OF COURSE—ZOMBIES!

MARVEL: Jim, you are developing quite a niche for yourself adapting Marvel adventures from abroad for a North American audience. Your work on the manga *Zombies Assemble* follows your earlier reinterpretation of the manhwa *Avengers K*. What makes you such a good fit for this kind of project?

ZUB: My fandom falls on the crossroads between my love of Marvel Comics and manga, so it's wonderful bringing both those elements into play. Before I started writing comics at Marvel, I worked for nine years as a project manager and editor at UDON, organizing and communicating with many different North American and foreign clients on publishing, video game, and media projects, including quite a few Japanese manga and art books. I'm also the writer and co-creator of *Wayward*, a creator-owned comic set in Japan with teenagers fighting traditional *yokai* monsters and spirits on the streets of modern Tokyo.

MARVEL: So it's fair to say you have a big interest in Japanese culture and fiction—does that extend to speaking the language at all?

ZUB: My Japanese language skills are pretty weak, unfortunately. I can do the meet-and-greet thing, counting, directions, and ordering basic food at a restaurant. Same with reading. Just the absolute basics. I've traveled to Japan multiple times and keep trying to use my meager language skills, but the country is becoming so much more tourist- and English-friendly that it's rarely needed, especially in the big cities.

MARVEL: Speaking of making things "English-friendly," that is exactly your job on *Zombies Assemble*. What does that process involve, and what form is the book in when you begin your work?

ZUB: I receive a really raw translation, very literal, that covers what the characters are saying. It's functional, but has very little personality. My job is to make the story read as smoothly as possible and make sure the characters sound like the ones readers expect to "hear." Captain America has to be that upstanding Sentinel of Liberty. Tony Stark is sarcastic and confident. Bruce Banner is reserved and a bit impatient. The overall dialogue and plot progression is the same as the original—I'm just making sure the characters reflect their movie counterparts. Thor's dialogue in the Japanese version is quite contemporary, so I've been bringing the mythic flair North American readers expect from the comics back into it. "Verily," "thine," and all that good stuff.

MARVEL: Forsooth! Is that, in some ways, more challenging than writing your own scripts from scratch?

ZUB: It's definitely a challenge because the panels, art, and dialogue balloons are already set. Barring some simple cosmetic changes, we can't alter much, so I have to work with the material as is. The meanings of words from Japanese to English aren't always one-to-one. Character intent, jokes, sarcasm—they all need to be adapted so English readers can enjoy the story and have the same reaction as Japanese readers.

MARVEL: One thing that takes some getting used to is reading the pages from right to left. Does that shape how you approach your dialogue?

ZUB: Reading manga in the traditional format is odd for North American readers at first, especially since you're reading each sentence inside the word balloons left to right even while going the opposite way moving from panel to panel. The toughest thing is when the original Japanese has lines of dialogue split in half for dramatic effect. Reworking those so they don't sound strange is important so readers aren't left wondering why a character's speech sounds stilted.

MARVEL: As for the story itself, super heroes vs. zombies is a beautifully simple concept, and one that Marvel has visited successfully a few times before. How would you sum up the appeal?

ZUB: Zombies as a whole are such an enduring horror trope because it feels frighteningly close at hand. The creatures aren't mythic monsters from afar—they're everyone all around you corrupted and relentless, pushing forth in a wave of destruction. Adding super heroes to that mix makes for an interesting contrast point. Aspirational, colorful characters fighting against grotesque hordes of humanity gone berserk.

STOP

FACE FRONT, TRUE BELIEVER!

This book is printed in traditional Japanese style, which means this is the back of the book! To read this manga, flip the book over and read from right to left, and within each panel from top to bottom (just like you would with an American comic).

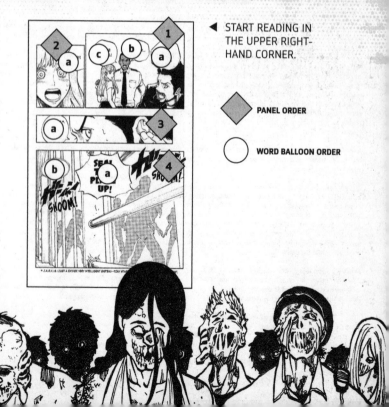

◀ START READING IN THE UPPER RIGHT-HAND CORNER.

PANEL ORDER

WORD BALLOON ORDER